Alison Bell's

GRADED PIECES FOR PIANO

BOOK 1 : VERY EASY

AMAZING GRACE, 16

AMONG MY SOUVENIRS, 14

BAA! BAA! BLACK SHEEP, 20

CHARLIE IS MY DARLING, 36

COLONEL BOGEY, 32

EDELWEISS, 22

ETERNAL FATHER STRONG TO SAVE, 21

JINGLE BELLS, 6

LITTLE BUTTERCUP, 11

LOCH LOMOND, 24

LOVE ME TENDER, 2

MORNING HAS BROKEN, 8

MY FAVOURITE THINGS, 27

NEARER MY GOD TO THEE, 38

OH, WHAT A BEAUTIFUL MORNIN', 18

POLLY PUT THE KETTLE ON, 26

SCARBOROUGH FAIR, 4

THEME FROM 'NEW WORLD SYMPHONY', 10

THREE LITTLE KITTENS, 34

WHAT SHALL WE DO WITH THE DRUNKEN SAILOR, 39

YE BANKS AND BRAES, 30

Wise Publications, London/New York/Sydney/Cologne

Exclusive Distributors:
Music Sales Limited, 8/9 Frith Street, London W1V 5TZ, England.
Music Sales Pty. Limited, 120 Rothschild Avenue, Rosebery, NSW 2018, Australia.

This book © Copyright 1983: Wise Publications
ISBN 0.7119.0036.1/Order No. AM 30297

Art Direction: Howard Brown. Photography: Peter Wood

Music Sales complete catalogue lists thousands of titles and is free from
your local music book shop, or direct from Music Sales Limited. Please send £1 in
stamps for postage to Music Sales Limited, 8/9 Frith Street, London W1V 5TZ.

Printed in England: J.B. Offset Printers (Marks Tey) Limited, Marks Tey.

LOVE ME TENDER

WORDS & MUSIC: ELVIS PRESLEY & VERA MATSON

3. Love me tender, love me dear;
   Tell me you are mine.
   I'll be yours through all the years,
   Till the end of time.
   Love me tender etc.

4. When at last my dreams come true,
   Darling this I know;
   Happiness will follow you
   Ev'rywhere you go.
   Love me tender etc.

SCARBOROUGH FAIR

WORDS & MUSIC: TRADITIONAL

JINGLE BELLS

WORDS & MUSIC: TRADITIONAL

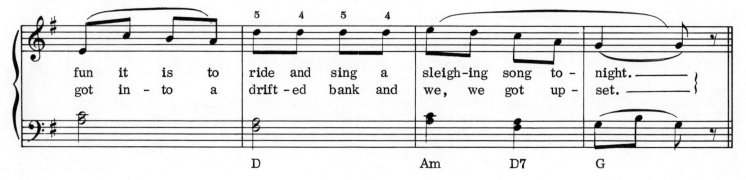

CHORUS

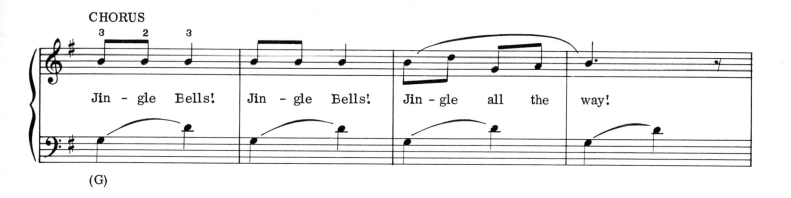

Jin - gle Bells! Jin - gle Bells! Jin - gle all the way!

(G)

Oh! what fun it is to ride in a one - horse o - pen sleigh! Oh!

C   G   A   D7

Jin - gle Bells! Jin - gle Bells! Jin - gle all the way!

G

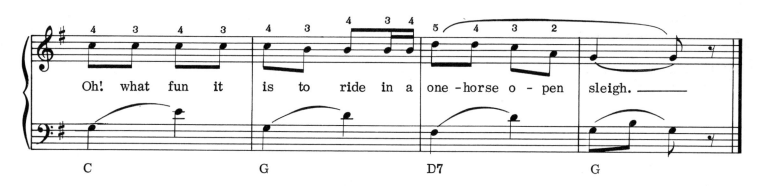

Oh! what fun it is to ride in a one - horse o - pen sleigh.

C   G   D7   G

3. Now the ground is white,
   Go it while you're young!
   Take the girls tonight
   And sing this sleighing song.
   Just get a bobtail'd bay,
   Two forty for his speed,
   Then hitch him to an open sleigh
   And crack! you'll take the lead.
   Jingle Bells etc.

MORNING HAS BROKEN

WORDS: ELEANOR FARJEON
MUSIC: CAT STEVENS

1. Morn - ing has bro - ken like the first morn - ing, Black - bird has spo - ken like the first bird.
2. Sweet the rain's new fall, like sun - lit from heav - en, Like the first dew - fall on the first grass.

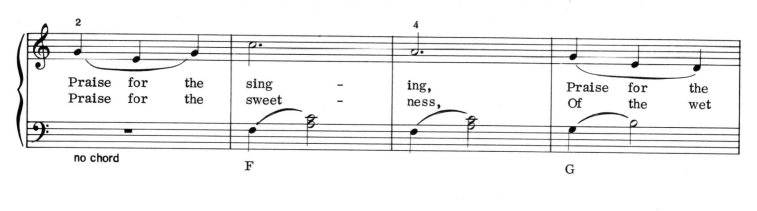

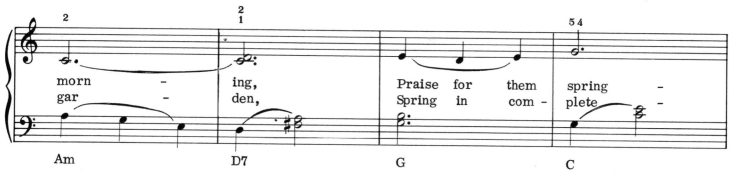

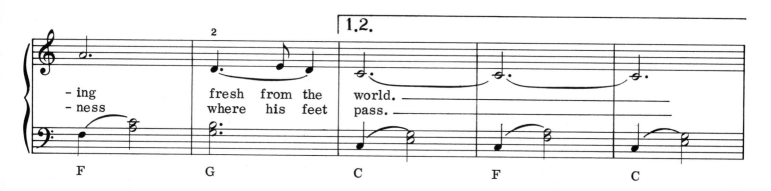

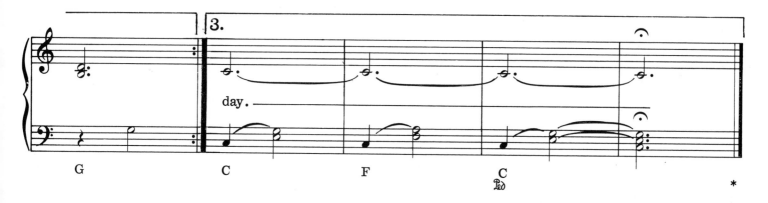

3. Mine is the sunlight,
   Mine is the morning,
   Born of the one light Eden saw play.
   Praise with elation,
   Praise ev'ry morning,
   God's recreation of the new day.

THEME FROM 'NEW WORLD SYMPHONY'

MUSIC: ANTONÍN DVOŘÁK

LITTLE BUTTERCUP

WORDS & MUSIC: TRADITIONAL

co - nies and   pret - ty   po - lo - nies and   ex - cel -lent   pep - per - mint

G   B7   Em   G   D7

drops. _____   Then   buy   of   your   But - ter - cup,   dear   lit - tle

G   C   G7   C

But - ter - cup,   sail - ors should   ne - ver   be   shy. _____   So

G7   C   F   C

buy   of   your   But - ter - cup,   poor   lit - tle   But - ter - cup,   Come,   of your

A   F   G   C

But - ter - cup   buy. _____   *f*

G   G7   C   G7   C

AMONG MY SOUVENIRS

WORDS: EDGAR LESLIE
MUSIC: HORATIO NICHOLLS

AMAZING GRACE
WORDS & MUSIC: TRADITIONAL

OH, WHAT A BEAUTIFUL MORNIN'

WORDS: OSCAR HAMMERSTEIN II
MUSIC: RICHARD RODGERS

BAA! BAA! BLACK SHEEP

WORDS & MUSIC: TRADITIONAL

ETERNAL FATHER STRONG TO SAVE

WORDS & MUSIC: TRADITIONAL

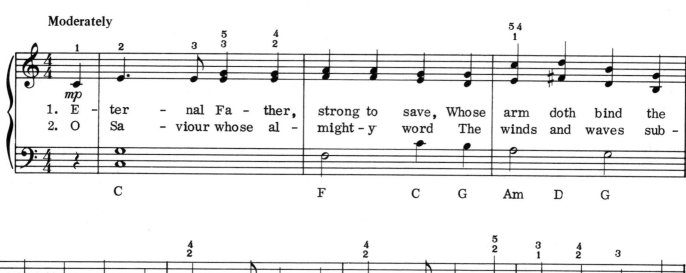

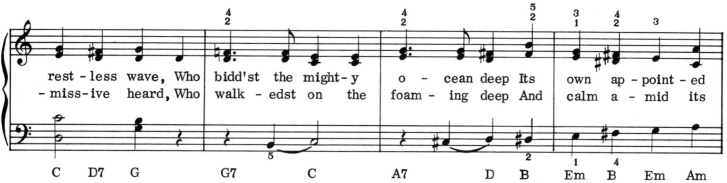

3. O sacred Spirit who didst brood
   Upon the waters dark and rude,
   And bid their angry tumult cease,
   And give, for wild confusion, peace:
   O hear us when we cry to Thee
   For those in peril on the sea.

4. O Trinity of love and power,
   Our brethren shield in danger's hour;
   From rock and tempest, fire and foe,
   Protect them wheresoe're they go;
   And ever let there rise to Thee
   Glad hymns of praise from land and sea.

EDELWEISS

WORDS: OSCAR HAMMERSTEIN II
MUSIC: RICHARD RODGERS

LOCH LOMOND

WORDS & MUSIC: TRADITIONAL

POLLY PUT THE KETTLE ON

WORDS & MUSIC: TRADITIONAL

MY FAVOURITE THINGS

WORDS: OSCAR HAMMERSTEIN II
MUSIC: RICHARD RODGERS

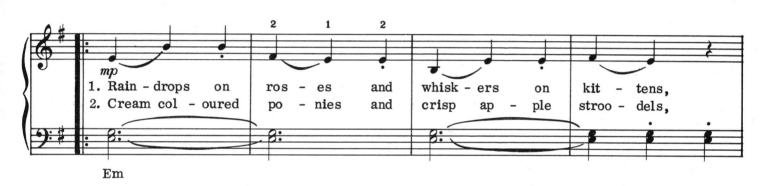

1. Rain - drops on ros - es and whisk - ers on kit - tens,
2. Cream col - oured po - nies and crisp ap - ple stroo - dels,

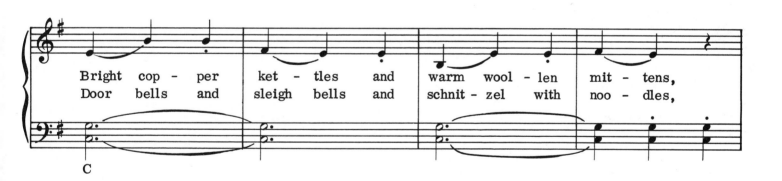

Bright cop - per ket - tles and warm wool - len mit - tens,
Door bells and sleigh bells and schnit - zel with noo - dles,

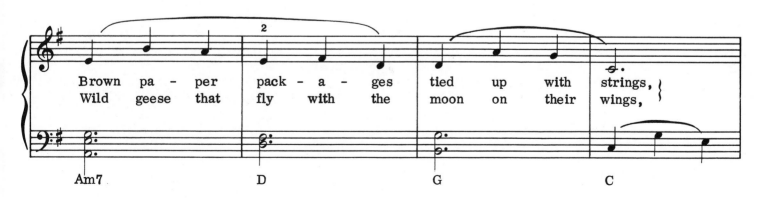

Brown pa - per pack - a - ges tied up with strings,
Wild geese that fly with the moon on their wings,

YE BANKS AND BRAES

WORDS & MUSIC: TRADITIONAL

COLONEL BOGEY

KENNETH J. ALFORD

THREE LITTLE KITTENS

WORDS & MUSIC: TRADITIONAL

Fairly Bright

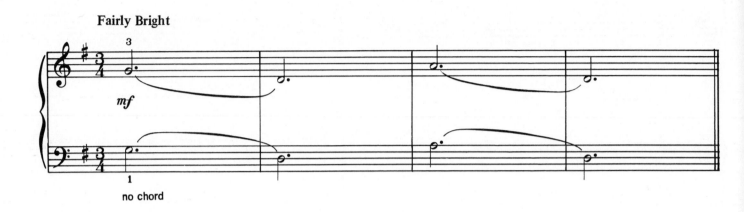

no chord

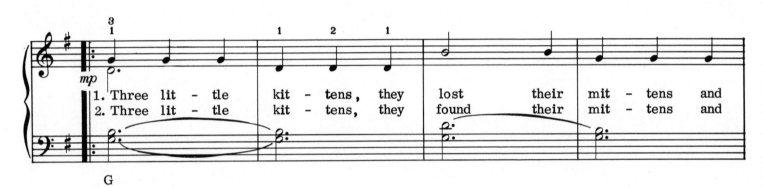

1. Three lit - tle kit - tens, they lost their mit - tens and
2. Three lit - tle kit - tens, they found their mit - tens and

G

they be - gan to cry. ——
they be - gan to laugh. ——

D7   G

"Mi - aow, mi - aow,
"Purr, purr, purr, purr,

CHARLIE IS MY DARLING

WORDS & MUSIC: TRADITIONAL

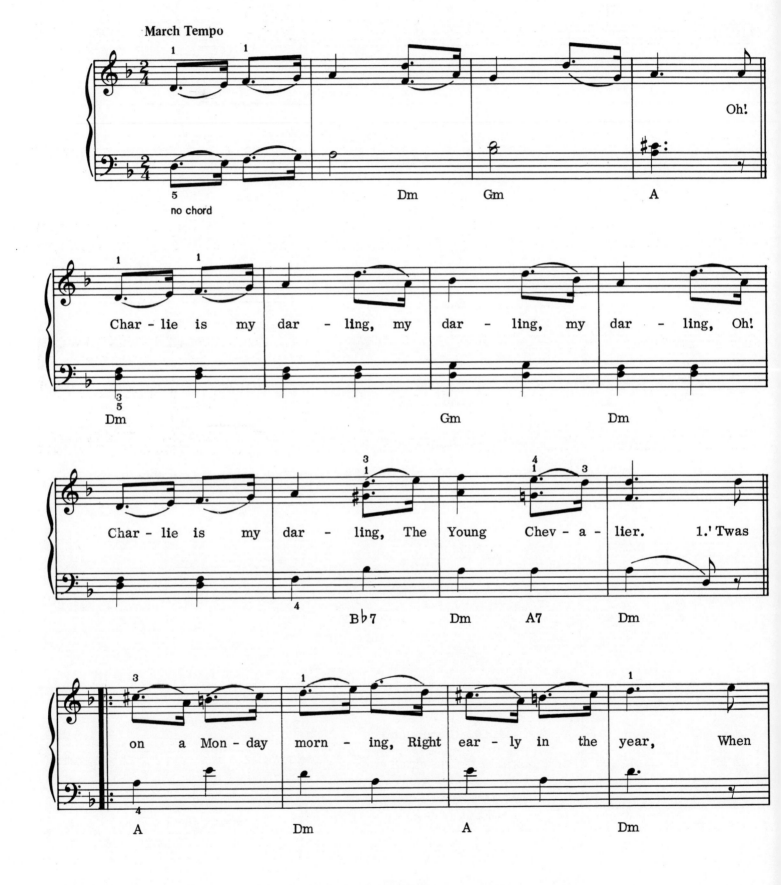

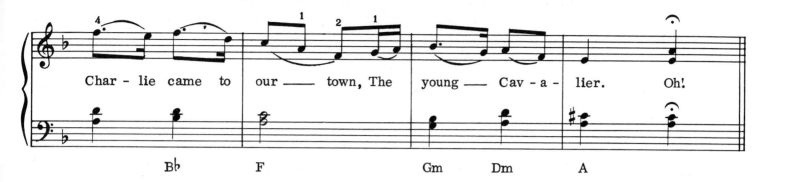

Char - lie came to our ____ town, The young ____ Cav - a - lier. Oh!

Bb   F   Gm   Dm   A

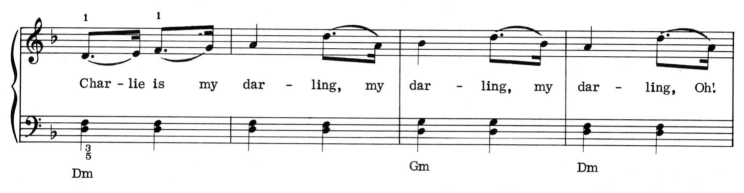

Char - lie is my dar - ling, my dar - ling, my dar - ling, Oh!

Dm   Gm   Dm

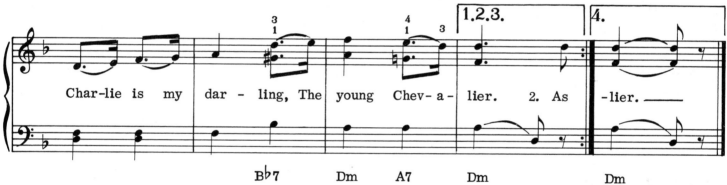

1.2.3.   4.

Char-lie is my dar - ling, The young Chev- a - lier. 2. As   -lier. ____

Bb7   Dm   A7   Dm   Dm

2. As he cam' marchin' up the street,
   The pipes play'd loud and clear,
   And a' the folk cam' rinnin' out
   To meet the Chevalier.
          Oh! Charlie etc.

3. Wi' Hieland bonnets on their heads,
   And claymores bright and clear;
   They cam' to fight for Scotland's lord,
   The young Chevalier.
          Oh! Charlie etc.

4. They've left their bonnie Hieland hills,
   Their wives and bairnies dear,
   To draw the sword for Scotland's lord,
   The young Chevalier.
          Oh! Charlie etc.

NEARER MY GOD TO THEE

WORDS & MUSIC: TRADITIONAL

3. There let the way appear,
Steps unto heaven;
All that Thou sendest me
In mercy given:
Angels to beckon me
Nearer, my God, to Thee,
Nearer to Thee!

4. Then, with my walking thoughts
Bright with thy praise,
Out of my stony griefs,
Bethel I'll raise;
So by my woes to be
Nearer, my God, to Thee,
Nearer to Thee!

5. Or if on joyful wing
Cleaving the sky,
Sun, moon and stars forget,
Upwards I fly;
Still all my song shall be,
Nearer, my God, to Thee,
Nearer to Thee!

WHAT SHALL WE DO WITH THE DRUNKEN SAILOR

WORDS & MUSIC: TRADITIONAL

12/89   9671